Edexcel Topic A-Level Mathematics

Core Mathematics 1 and Core Mathematics 2

✱ Make sure CDRom is returned

Student Book and CD-ROM

CONTENTS

CD CONTENTS

6663 Paper 1: May 2006
6664 Paper 1: May 2006
Topic Tutor model solutions to all exercise questions

A PEARSON COMPANY

Published by:
Edexcel Limited
One90 High Holborn
London WC1V 7BH

www.edexcel.org.uk

Distributed by:
Pearson Education Limited
Edinburgh Gate
Harlow
Essex CM20 2JE

First published 2006
ISBN 978-1-84690-011-2

Cover design by Youngs Design Ltd
Questions and answers typeset by Gaelle Anderson
Topic Tutor model solutions produced by Live Learning Technologies Ltd
Series directed by Mark Jordan

With thanks to the series production team:
John Barrett, Rosemary Smith, Richard Taylor, Ian Youngs
Clare Berryman, Sacha Harmsworth, Michelle Hessels, Helen Pritt, Mark Ralph

Printed and bound in Great Britain by Bell & Bain Limited

CD-ROM reproduction in Germany by Optimal

The Publisher's policy is to use paper manufactured from sustainable forests.

Introduction

Welcome to *Edexcel Topic Tutor*, a resource to support learning and revision in the most popular A-level units of the Edexcel course.

This book contains a series of topic tests using real past exam questions, which can be tackled in class, as homework or as part of your revision. Next to each exercise title there is a reference to the relevant chapters in Edexcel endorsed textbooks by Longman (AS Core for Edexcel, ISBN 0-582-84237-9) and Heinemann (Modular Maths for Edexcel AS and A-Level Core Book 1, ISBN 0-435-51097-8, and Modular Maths for Edexcel AS and A-Level Core Book 2, ISBN 0-435-51098-5). Short answers at the back of the book allow you to quickly spot problem areas. Where you need extra help, you can use the accompanying CD-ROM to view animated model answers with commentary from examiners.

The book also includes two unit exam papers for additional practice. Answers to these and other Edexcel examination papers are available at: www.examzone.com

Getting started

Insert the disk into your CD-ROM drive. Edexcel Topic Tutor should auto-run on your PC. If it does not auto run, click Start, My Computer, and right-click on the CD-ROM icon and choose 'Explore'. Double click on the Tutor.exe application and follow the onscreen instructions.

If you are a Mac user, you will need to double-click the CD icon on the desktop and double-click on the Topic Tutor application.

Animated model solutions are provided for all exercises. To see and hear a worked solution to a question you will need to:

1.   Click on the exercise name from the menu of exercises (a numbered list of answers will appear)

2.   Click the relevant answer number/part

This will open the Live Learning Player. You can click through the many steps of a solution or replay it using the control buttons at the bottom of the Live Learning Player.

You can view brief answers for any question by clicking on the 'Answers' link on the main screen.

You can view select past exam papers by clicking on the links at the bottom of the screen. You will need Adobe® Acrobat® Reader® installed on your machine or network in order to view both the answer PDFs and the sample paper PDFs. If you do not have Adobe® Acrobat® Reader®, follow the installation instructions on the Help screen.

Taking the Topic Tests

The number of marks available for a question is shown beside each question or question part.

You can check the answers to each question in the answer section at the end of each unit.

Using the Practice Examination Papers

On the front page of each examination paper there are details about the examination you are taking, such as the amount of time in which you must answer the questions.

All questions have space in which to write your final answer and some have space in which to show your working.

Hardware Requirements

- Operating system: Windows 95(OS R2), 98, ME, 2000, NT or XP
- Pentium 400 (IBM Compatible PC) or equivalent PC
- 128 MB RAM or higher
- 16 bit graphics card
- CD-ROM drive (minimum 16 speed recommended)
- SVGA colour monitor and 1024/768 resolution
- Sound card
- At least 100 MB free hard disk space

Mac System requirements

- Operating system: X 10.1.5 or higher
- 500MHz G4 processor
- 256MB of RAM or higher
- 450MB of free hard disk space
- 16 speed CD ROM drive
- 16 bit colour monitor set at 1024/768 resolution

Technical support and advice is available from the Ask Edexcel service at www.edexcel.org.uk/ask.

Core Mathematics C1

Contents

Core Mathematics C1 - Formulae

Mensuration

Surface area of sphere $= 4\pi r^2$

Area of curved surface of cone $= \pi r \times$ slant height

Arithmetic series

$u_n = a + (n-1)d$

$S_n = \dfrac{1}{2}n(a+l) = \dfrac{1}{2}n[2a + (n-1)d]$

A - Algebra and functions

1. (*a*) Write $\sqrt{45}$ in the form $a\sqrt{5}$, where a is an integer.

(1)

(*b*) Express $\dfrac{2(3+\sqrt{5})}{(3-\sqrt{5})}$ in the form $b + c\sqrt{5}$, where b and c are integers.

(5)

2.

$$x^2 + 2x + 3 \equiv (x + a)^2 + b.$$

(*a*) Find the values of the constants a and b.

(2)

(*b*) Sketch the graph of $y = x^2 + 2x + 3$, indicating clearly the coordinates of any intersections with the coordinate axes.

(3)

(*c*) Find the value of the discriminant of $x^2 + 2x + 3$. Explain how the sign of the discriminant relates to your sketch in part (*b*).

(2)

The equation $x^2 + kx + 3 = 0$, where k is a constant, has no real roots.

(*d*) Find the set of possible values of k, giving your answer in surd form.

(4)

3.

$$x^2 - 8x - 29 \equiv (x + a)^2 + b,$$

where a and b are constants.

(*a*) Find the value of a and the value of b.

(3)

(*b*) Hence, or otherwise, show that the roots of

$$x^2 - 8x - 29 = 0$$

are $c \pm d\sqrt{5}$, where c and d are integers to be found.

(3)

4. The curve C has equation $y = x^2 - 4$ and the straight line l has equation $y + 3x = 0$.

(a) Sketch C and l on the same axes.

(3)

(b) Write down the coordinates of the points at which C meets the coordinate axes.

(2)

(c) Using algebra, find the coordinates of the points at which l intersects C.

(4)

5. Solve the simultaneous equations

$$x + y = 3,$$

$$x^2 + y = 15.$$

(6)

6. The width of a rectangular sports pitch is x metres, $x > 0$. The length of the pitch is 20 m more than its width. Given that the perimeter of the pitch must be less than 300 m,

(a) form a linear inequality in x.

(2)

Given that the area of the pitch must be greater than 4800 m^2,

(b) form a quadratic inequality in x.

(2)

(c) by solving your inequalities, find the set of possible values of x.

(4)

7. Factorise completely
$$x^3 - 4x^2 + 3x.$$

(3)

8.

Figure 1

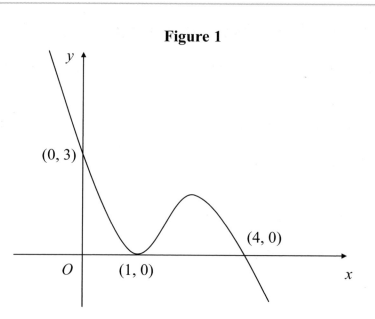

Figure 1 shows a sketch of the curve with equation $y = f(x)$. The curve passes through the points $(0, 3)$ and $(4, 0)$ and touches the x-axis at the point $(1, 0)$.

On separate diagrams, sketch the curve with equation

(a) $y = f(x + 1)$,

(3)

(b) $y = 2f(x)$,

(3)

(c) $y = f\left(\dfrac{1}{2}x\right)$.

(3)

On each diagram show clearly the coordinates of all the points at which the curve meets the axes.

B - Coordinate geometry

L: 6 H: 5

1. The line L has equation $y = 5 - 2x$.

(a) Show that the point P $(3, -1)$ lies on L.

(1)

(b) Find an equation of the line perpendicular to L, which passes through P. Give your answer in the form $ax + by + c = 0$, where a, b and c are integers.

(4)

2. The line l_1 passes through the point $(9, -4)$ and has gradient $\frac{1}{3}$.

(a) Find an equation for l_1 in the form $ax + by + c = 0$, where a, b and c are integers.

(3)

The line l_2 passes through the origin O and has gradient -2. The lines l_1 and l_2 intersect at the point P.

(b) Calculate the coordinates of P.

(4)

Given that l_1 crosses the y-axis at the point C,

(c) calculate the exact area of $\triangle OCP$.

(3)

3.

Figure 2

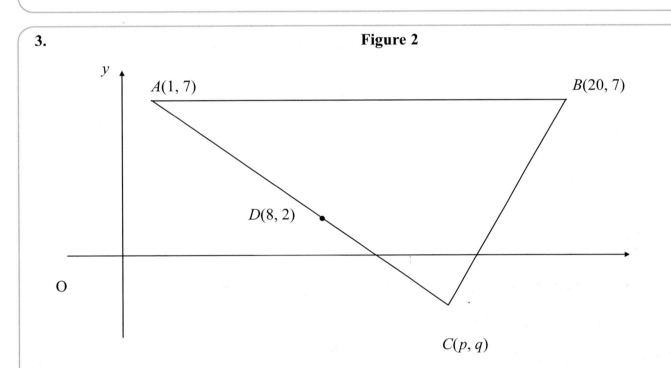

The points $A(1, 7)$, $B(20, 7)$ and $C(p, q)$ form the vertices of a triangle ABC, as shown in Figure 2. The point $D(8, 2)$ is the mid-point of AC.

(a) Find the value of p and the value of q.

(2)

The line l, which passes through D and is perpendicular to AC, intersects AB at E.

(b) Find an equation for l, in the form $ax + by + c = 0$, where a, b and c are integers.

(5)

(c) Find the exact x-coordinate of E.

(2)

C - Sequences and series

1. The sequence u_1, u_2, u_3, ... , is defined by the recurrence relation

$$u_{n+1} = (-1)^n u_n + d, \quad u_1 = 2, \quad \text{where } d \text{ is a constant.}$$

(*a*) Show that $u_5 = 2$.

(4)

(*b*) Deduce an expression for u_{10}, in terms of d.

(1)

Given that $u_3 = 3u_2$,

(*c*) find the value of d.

(2)

2. An arithmetic series has first term a and common difference d.

(*a*) Prove that the sum of the first n terms of the series is

$$\tfrac{1}{2} n[2a + (n-1)d\,].$$

(4)

The rth term of a sequence is $(5r - 2)$.

(*b*) Write down the first, second and third terms of this sequence.

(1)

(*c*) Show that $\displaystyle\sum_{r=1}^{n}(5r-2) = \frac{1}{2}n(5n+1).$

(3)

(*d*) Hence, or otherwise, find the value of $\displaystyle\sum_{r=5}^{200}(5r-2)$.

(4)

3. On Alice's 11th birthday she started to receive an annual allowance. The first annual allowance was £500 and on each following birthday the allowance was increased by £200.

(*a*) Show that, immediately after her 12th birthday, the total of the allowances that Alice had received was £1200.

(1)

(*b*) Find the amount of Alice's annual allowance on her 18th birthday.

(2)

(*c*) Find the total of the allowances that Alice had received up to and including her 18th birthday.

(3)

When the total of the allowances that Alice had received reached £32 000 the allowance stopped.

(*d*) Find how old Alice was when she received her last allowance.

(7)

D - Differentiation

1. Given that $y = 2x^2 - \dfrac{6}{x^3}$, $x \neq 0$, find $\dfrac{dy}{dx}$,

(2)

2. Given that $y = 5x^3 + 7x + 3$, find

   (a) $\dfrac{dy}{dx}$,

   (3)

   (b) $\dfrac{d^2y}{dx^2}$

   (1)

3.

Figure 2

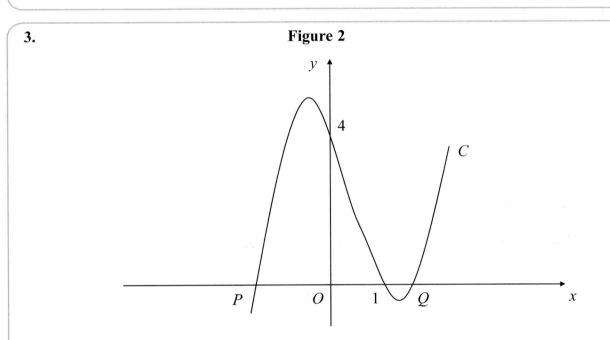

Figure 2 shows part of the curve C with equation $y = (x - 1)(x^2 - 4)$.

The curve cuts the x-axis at the points P, $(1, 0)$ and Q, as shown in Figure 2.

(a) Write down the x-coordinate of P and the x-coordinate of Q.

(2)

(b) Show that $\dfrac{dy}{dx} = 3x^2 - 2x - 4$.

(3)

(c) Show that $y = x + 7$ is an equation of the tangent to C at the point $(-1, 6)$.

(2)

The tangent to C at the point R is parallel to the tangent at the point $(-1, 6)$.

(d) Find the exact coordinates of R.

(5)

4. The curve C has equation $y = \frac{1}{3}x^3 - 4x^2 + 8x + 3$.

The point P has coordinates $(3, 0)$.

(*a*) Show that P lies on C.

(1)

(*b*) Find the equation of the tangent to C at P, giving your answer in the form $y = mx + c$, where m and c are constants.

(5)

Another point Q also lies on C. The tangent to C at Q is parallel to the tangent to C at P.

(*c*) Find the coordinates of Q.

(5)

E - Integration

1. Given that $y = 2x^2 - \dfrac{6}{x^3}$, $x \neq 0$, find $\displaystyle\int y \; dx$.

(2)

2. Find $\displaystyle\int \left(1 + 3\sqrt{x} - \dfrac{1}{x^2}\right) dx$.

(4)

3. (*a*) Show that $\dfrac{(3 - \sqrt{x})^2}{\sqrt{x}}$ can be written as $9x^{-\frac{1}{2}} - 6 + x^{\frac{1}{2}}$.

(2)

Given that $\dfrac{dy}{dx} = \dfrac{(3 - \sqrt{x})^2}{\sqrt{x}}$, $x > 0$, and that $y = \frac{2}{3}$ at $x = 1$,

(*b*) find y in terms of x.

(6)

4. The curve with equation $y = f(x)$ passes through the point $(1, 6)$. Given that

$$f'(x) = 3 + \frac{5x^2 + 2}{x^{\frac{1}{2}}}, \quad x > 0,$$

find $f(x)$ and simplify your answer.

(7)

Core Mathematics C1 - Answers

A - Algebra and functions

1. (a) $3\sqrt{5}$

    (b) $7 + 3\sqrt{5}$

2. (a) $a = 1, b = 2$

    (b)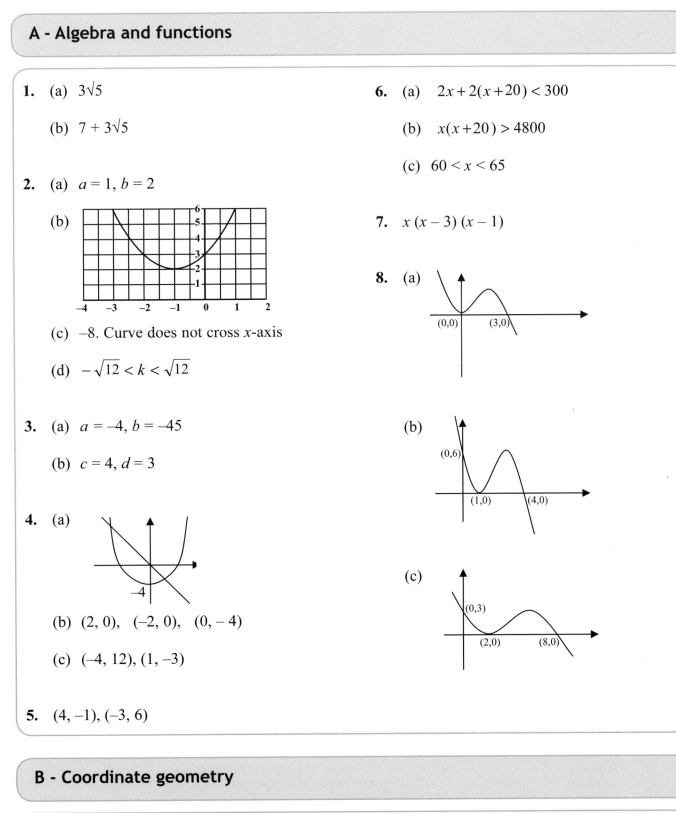

    (c) -8. Curve does not cross x-axis

    (d) $-\sqrt{12} < k < \sqrt{12}$

3. (a) $a = -4, b = -45$

    (b) $c = 4, d = 3$

4. (a)

    (b) $(2, 0), \ (-2, 0), \ (0, -4)$

    (c) $(-4, 12), (1, -3)$

5. $(4, -1), (-3, 6)$

6. (a) $2x + 2(x + 20) < 300$

    (b) $x(x + 20) > 4800$

    (c) $60 < x < 65$

7. $x \, (x - 3) \, (x - 1)$

8. (a)

    (b)

    (c)

B - Coordinate geometry

1. (a) $y = 5 - (2 \times 3) = -1$

    (b) $x - 2y - 5 = 0$

2. (a) $3y - x + 21 = 0$

    (b) $(3, -6)$

    (c) 10.5

3. (a) $p = 15, \quad q = -3$

    (b) $7x - 5y - 46 = 0$

    (c) $11\dfrac{4}{7}$ or $\dfrac{81}{7}$

C - Sequences and series

1. (a) $u_2 = (-1)(2) + d = -2 + d$

          $u_3 = (-1)^2(-2 + d) + d = -2 + 2d$

          $u_4 = (-1)^3(-2 + 2d) + d = 2 - d$

          $u_5 = (-1)^4(2 - d) + d = 2$

    (b) $d - 2$

    (c) 4

2. (a) $S = a + (a+d) + (a+2d) + \ldots + [a+(n-1)d]$

         $S = [a + (n-1)d] + [a + (n-2)d] + \ldots + a$

                             or equiv.

      Add: $2S = n[2a + (n-1)d] \Rightarrow$

                 $S = \frac{1}{2} n[2a + (n-1)d]$

    (b) 3, 8, 13

    (c) $a = 3$ $d = 5$

       $\text{Sum} = \frac{1}{2}n[(2 \times 3) + 5(n-1)] = \frac{1}{2}n(5n+1)$

    (d) 100 058

3. (a) $500 + (500 + 200) = 1200$

       or $S_2 = \frac{1}{2}2\{1000 + 200\} = 1200$

    (b) £1 900

    (c) £9 600

    (d) 26

D - Differentiation

1. $\frac{dy}{dx} = 4x + 18x^{-4}$

2. (a) $15x^2 + 7$

    (b) $30x$

3. (a) $-2 \ (P), \quad 2 \ (Q)$

    (b) $y = x^3 - x^2 - 4x + 4$

       $\Rightarrow \frac{dy}{dx} = 3x^2 - 2x - 4$

    (c) at $C \ \frac{dy}{dx} = 3(-1)^2 - 2(-1) - 4 = 1$

       $y = 1x + c$ and so $6 = -1 + c \Rightarrow c = 7$

    (d) $3x^2 - 2x - 4 = 1$

       $3x^2 - 2x - 5 = 0$

       $x = +1$ or $-\frac{5}{3}$

       $\left(-\frac{5}{3}, -\frac{22}{27}\right)$

4. (a) $\frac{1}{3}(27) - 4(9) + 8(3) + 3 = 0$

    (b) $\frac{dy}{dx} = x^2 - 8x + 8$

       at $P \ \frac{dy}{dx} = -7 = m$

       $y = -7x + c$ and $0 = -7(3) + c$

                        $c = 21$

       $y = -7x + 21$

    (c) at $Q \ \frac{dy}{dx} = -7$

       $\Rightarrow x^2 - 8x + 8 = -7$

       $\Rightarrow x = 3(P)$ or $5(Q)$

       Q is $\left(5, -\frac{46}{3}\right)$

E - Integration

1. $\dfrac{2x^3}{3} - \dfrac{6x^{-2}}{-2} + C$

2. $x + 2x^{\frac{3}{2}} + x^{-1} + C$

3. (c) $(3 - \sqrt{x})^2 = 9 - 6\sqrt{x} + x$

$(\div \; by \; \sqrt{x}) \; \rightarrow 9x^{-\frac{1}{2}} - 6 + x^{\frac{1}{2}}$

(b) $\quad y = 18x^{\frac{1}{2}} - 6x + \dfrac{2}{3}x^{\frac{3}{2}} - 12$

4. $\quad 3x + 2x^{\frac{5}{2}} + 4x^{\frac{1}{2}} - 3$

Core Mathematics C1 - Practice paper

Answers to these practice papers have not been included in this book. Your teacher should have access to the mark schemes through Edexcel Online. Alternatively, visit www.examzone.co.uk to download model answers.

Paper Reference(s)

6663/01

Edexcel GCE

Core Mathematics C1

Advanced Subsidiary

Monday 22 May 2006 – Morning

Time: 1 hour 30 minutes

Materials required for examination	**Items included with question papers**
Mathematical Formulae (Green)	Nil

Calculators may NOT be used in this examination.

Instructions to Candidates

In the boxes above, write your centre number, candidate number, your surname, initial(s) and signature.
Check that you have the correct question paper.
You must write your answer for each question in the space following the question.

Information for Candidates

Full marks may be obtained for answers to ALL questions.
The marks for individual questions and the parts of questions are shown in round brackets: e.g. **(2)**.
There are 11 questions in this question paper. The total mark for this paper is 75.

Advice to Candidates

You must ensure that your answers to parts of questions are clearly labelled.
You must show sufficient working to make your methods clear to the examiner. Answers without working may gain no credit.

1. Find $\int \left(6x^2 + 2 + x^{-\frac{1}{2}} \right) dx$, giving each term in its simplest form.

(4)

2. Find the set of values of x for which

$$x^2 - 7x - 18 > 0.$$

(4)

Leave
blank

3. On separate diagrams, sketch the graphs of

(a) $y = (x + 3)^2$,

(3)

(b) $y = (x + 3)^2 + k$, where k is a positive constant.

(2)

Show on each sketch the coordinates of each point at which the graph meets the axes.

4. A sequence $a_1, a_2, a_3, \ldots$ is defined by

$$a_1 = 3,$$
$$a_{n+1} = 3a_n - 5, \quad n \geqslant 1.$$

(a) Find the value of a_2 and the value of a_3.

(2)

(b) Calculate the value of $\displaystyle\sum_{r=1}^{5} a_r$.

(3)

Question 4 continued

5. Differentiate with respect to x

    (a) $x^4 + 6\sqrt{x}$,

                                                   (3)

    (b) $\dfrac{(x+4)^2}{x}$.

                                                   (4)

Leave
blank

6. (a) Expand and simplify $(4 + \sqrt{3})(4 - \sqrt{3})$.

(2)

(b) Express $\dfrac{26}{4 + \sqrt{3}}$ in the form $a + b\sqrt{3}$, where a and b are integers.

(2)

7. An athlete prepares for a race by completing a practice run on each of 11 consecutive days. On each day after the first day, he runs further than he ran on the previous day. The lengths of his 11 practice runs form an arithmetic sequence with first term a km and common difference d km.

He runs 9 km on the 11th day, and he runs a total of 77 km over the 11 day period.

Find the value of a and the value of d.

(7)

8. The equation $x^2 + 2px + (3p + 4) = 0$, where p is a positive constant, has equal roots.

(a) Find the value of p.

(4)

(b) For this value of p, solve the equation $x^2 + 2px + (3p + 4) = 0$.

(2)

9. Given that $f(x) = (x^2 - 6x)(x - 2) + 3x$,

   (a) express $f(x)$ in the form $x(ax^2 + bx + c)$, where a, b and c are constants.

                      (3)

   (b) Hence factorise $f(x)$ completely.

                      (2)

   (c) Sketch the graph of $y = f(x)$, showing the coordinates of each point at which the graph meets the axes.

                      (3)

Leave
blank

Question 9 continued

10. The curve C with equation $y = f(x)$, $x \neq 0$, passes through the point $(3, 7\frac{1}{2})$.

Given that $f'(x) = 2x + \dfrac{3}{x^2}$,

(a) find $f(x)$.

(5)

(b) Verify that $f(-2) = 5$.

(1)

(c) Find an equation for the tangent to C at the point $(-2, 5)$, giving your answer in the form $ax + by + c = 0$, where a, b and c are integers.

(4)

Question 10 continued

Leave blank

11. The line l_1 passes through the points $P(-1, 2)$ and $Q(11, 8)$.

(a) Find an equation for l_1 in the form $y = mx + c$, where m and c are constants.

(4)

The line l_2 passes through the point $R(10, 0)$ and is perpendicular to l_1. The lines l_1 and l_2 intersect at the point S.

(b) Calculate the coordinates of S.

(5)

(c) Show that the length of RS is $3\sqrt{5}$.

(2)

(d) Hence, or otherwise, find the exact area of triangle PQR.

(4)

Question 11 continued

TOTAL FOR PAPER: 75 MARKS

END

Core Mathematics C2

Contents

Core Mathematics C2 - Formulae

Candidates sitting C2 may also require those formulae listed under Core Mathematics C1.

Cosine rule

$$a^2 = b^2 + c^2 - 2bc \cos A$$

Binomial series

$$(a+b)^n = a^n + \binom{n}{1}a^{n-1}b + \binom{n}{2}a^{n-2}b^2 + \ldots + \binom{n}{r}a^{n-r}b^r + \ldots + b^n \quad (n \in \mathbb{N})$$

$$\text{where } \binom{n}{r} = {}^nC_r = \frac{n!}{r!(n-r)!}$$

$$(1+x)^n = 1 + nx + \frac{n(n-1)}{1 \times 2}x^2 + \ldots + \frac{n(n-1)\ldots(n-r+1)}{1 \times 2 \times \ldots \times r}x^r + \ldots \quad (|x| < 1, n \in \mathbb{R})$$

Logarithms and exponentials

$$\log_a x = \frac{\log_b x}{\log_b a}$$

Geometric series

$$u_n = ar^{n-1}$$

$$S_n = \frac{a(1-r^n)}{1-r}$$

$$S_\infty = \frac{a}{1-r} \text{ for } |r| < 1$$

Numerical integration

The trapezium rule: $\int_a^b y \ dx \approx \frac{1}{2}h\{(y_0 + y_n) + 2(y_1 + y_2 + \ldots + y_{n-1})\}$, where $h = \dfrac{b-a}{n}$

A - Algebra and functions

L: 12 H: 1

1. $f(x) = 2x^3 - x^2 + ax + b$, where a and b are constants.

It is given that $(x - 2)$ is a factor of f(x).

When f(x) is divided by $(x + 1)$, the remainder is 6.

Find the value of a and the value of b.

(7)

2. $f(x) = 2x^3 + x^2 - 5x + c$, where c is a constant.

Given that f(1) = 0,

(*a*) find the value of c,

(2)

(*b*) factorise f(x) completely,

(4)

(*c*) find the remainder when f(x) is divided by $(2x - 3)$.

(2)

B - Coordinate geometry

L: 13 H: 4

1. A circle C has radius $\sqrt{5}$ and has its centre at the point with coordinates $(4, 3)$.

(*a*) Prove that an equation of the circle C is $x^2 + y^2 - 8x - 6y + 20 = 0$

(3)

The line l, with equation $y = 2x$, is a tangent to the circle C.

(*b*) Find the coordinates of the point where the line l touches C.

(4)

2.

Figure 1

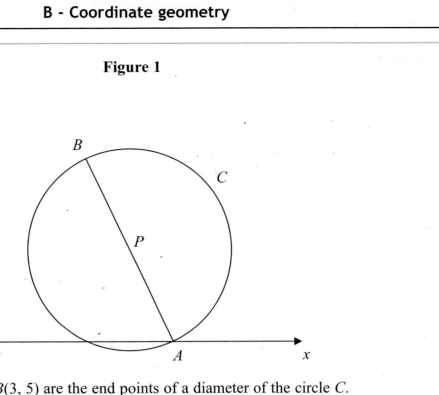

In Figure 1, $A(4, 0)$ and $B(3, 5)$ are the end points of a diameter of the circle C.

Find

(a) the exact length of AB,

(2)

(b) the coordinates of the midpoint P of AB,

(2)

(c) an equation for the circle C.

(3)

3. The circle C, with centre at the point A, has equation $x^2 + y^2 - 10x + 9 = 0$.

Find

(a) the coordinates of A,

(2)

(b) the radius of C,

(2)

(c) the coordinates of the points at which C crosses the x-axis.

(2)

Given that the line l with gradient $\dfrac{7}{2}$ is a tangent to C, and that l touches C at the point T,

(d) find an equation of the line which passes through A and T.

(3)

C - Sequences and series   *L: 14, 20 H: 5, 7*

1. A geometric series is $a + ar + ar^2 + \ldots$

(*a*) Prove that the sum of the first n terms of this series is

$$S_n = \frac{a(1-r^n)}{1-r}.$$

     (4)

The first and second terms of a geometric series G are 10 and 9 respectively.

(*b*) Find, to 3 significant figures, the sum of the first twenty terms of G.

     (3)

(*c*) Find the sum to infinity of G.

     (2)

Another geometric series has its first term equal to its common ratio. The sum to infinity of this series is 10.

(*d*) Find the exact value of the common ratio of this series.

     (3)

---

2. The first term of a geometric series is 120. The sum to infinity of the series is 480.

(*a*) Show that the common ratio, r, is $\dfrac{3}{4}$.

     (3)

(*b*) Find, to 2 decimal places, the difference between the 5th and 6th terms.

     (2)

(*c*) Calculate the sum of the first 7 terms.

     (2)

The sum of the first n terms of the series is greater than 300.

(*d*) Calculate the smallest possible value of n.

     (4)

---

3. (*a*) Write down the binomial expansion, in ascending powers of x, of $(1 + 6x)^4$, giving each coefficient as an integer.

     (3)

(*b*) Use your binomial expansion to find the exact value of 601^4.

     (2)

4. (a) Find the first 3 terms, in ascending powers of x, of the binomial expansion of

$$(1 + px)^9,$$

where p is a constant.

(2)

The first 3 terms are 1, $36x$ and $qx2$, where q is a constant.

(b) Find the value of p and the value of q.

(4)

D - Trigonometry

L: 16, 17 H: 2, 6, 8, 10

1. In the triangle ABC, $AB = 8$ cm, $AC = 7$ cm, $\angle ABC = 0.5$ radians and $\angle ACB = x$ radians.

    (*a*) Use the sine rule to find the value of $\sin x$, giving your answer to 3 decimal places.

    (3)

    Given that there are two possible values of x,

    (*b*) find these values of x, giving your answers to 2 decimal places.

    (3)

2.

Figure 2

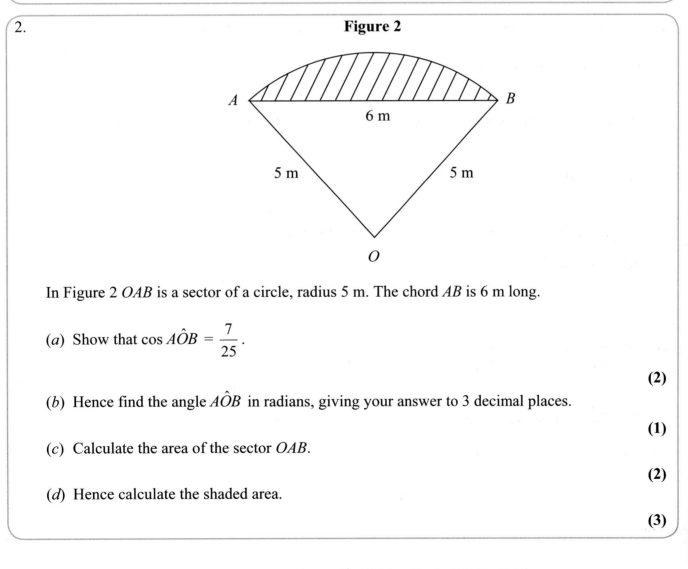

6 m

5 m   5 m

O

In Figure 2 OAB is a sector of a circle, radius 5 m. The chord AB is 6 m long.

(*a*) Show that $\cos A\hat{O}B = \dfrac{7}{25}$.

(2)

(*b*) Hence find the angle $A\hat{O}B$ in radians, giving your answer to 3 decimal places.

(1)

(*c*) Calculate the area of the sector OAB.

(2)

(*d*) Hence calculate the shaded area.

(3)

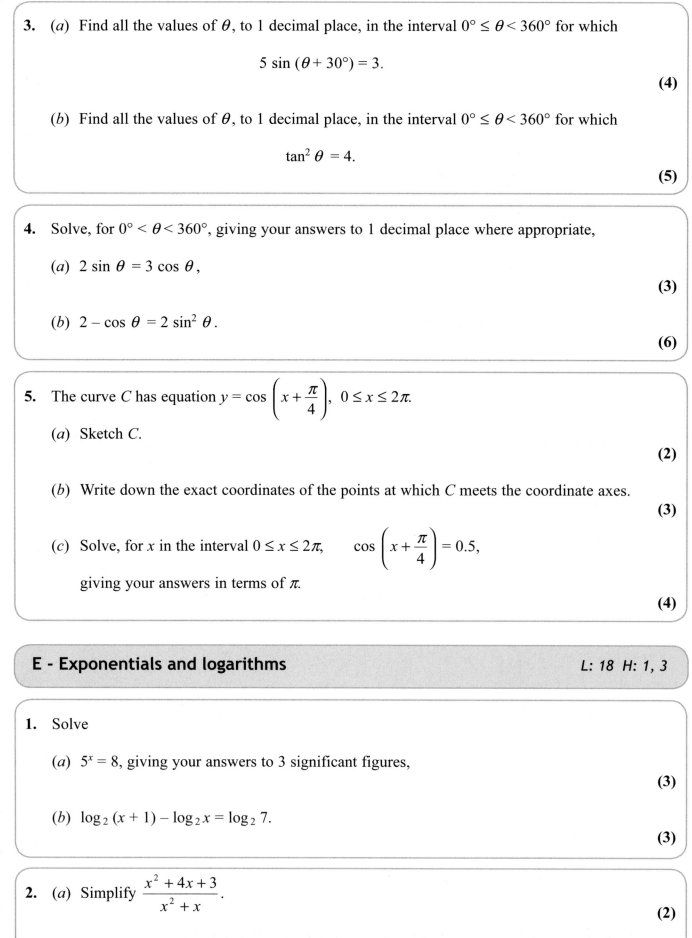

3. (a) Find all the values of θ, to 1 decimal place, in the interval $0° \le \theta < 360°$ for which

$$5 \sin (\theta + 30°) = 3.$$

(4)

(b) Find all the values of θ, to 1 decimal place, in the interval $0° \le \theta < 360°$ for which

$$\tan^2 \theta = 4.$$

(5)

4. Solve, for $0° < \theta < 360°$, giving your answers to 1 decimal place where appropriate,

(a) $2 \sin \theta = 3 \cos \theta$,

(3)

(b) $2 - \cos \theta = 2 \sin^2 \theta$.

(6)

5. The curve C has equation $y = \cos \left(x + \dfrac{\pi}{4} \right)$, $0 \le x \le 2\pi$.

(a) Sketch C.

(2)

(b) Write down the exact coordinates of the points at which C meets the coordinate axes.

(3)

(c) Solve, for x in the interval $0 \le x \le 2\pi$, $\cos \left(x + \dfrac{\pi}{4} \right) = 0.5$,

giving your answers in terms of π.

(4)

E - Exponentials and logarithms

L: 18 H: 1, 3

1. Solve

(a) $5^x = 8$, giving your answers to 3 significant figures,

(3)

(b) $\log_2 (x + 1) - \log_2 x = \log_2 7$.

(3)

2. (a) Simplify $\dfrac{x^2 + 4x + 3}{x^2 + x}$.

(2)

(b) Find the value of x for which $\log_2 (x^2 + 4x + 3) - \log_2 (x^2 + x) = 4$.

(4)

3. Given that $\log_5 x = a$ and $\log_5 y = b$, find in terms of a and b,

   (a) $\log_5\left(\dfrac{x^2}{y}\right)$,

   (2)

   (b) $\log_5(25x\sqrt{y})$.

   (3)

   It is given that $\log_5\left(\dfrac{x^2}{y}\right) = 1$ and that $\log_5(25x\sqrt{y}) = 1$.

   (c) Form simultaneous equations in a and b.

   (1)

   (d) Show that $a = -0.25$ and find the value of b

   (2)

   Using the value of a and b, or otherwise,

   (e) calculate, to 3 decimal places, the value of x and the value of y.

   (3)

F - Differentiation
L: 15 H: 9

1. The curve C has equation $\quad y = 2x^3 - 5x^2 - 4x + 2.$

   (a) Find $\dfrac{dy}{dx}$.

   (2)

   (b) Using the result from part (a), find the coordinates of the turning points of C.

   (4)

   (c) Find $\dfrac{d^2y}{dx^2}$.

   (2)

   (d) Hence, or otherwise, determine the nature of the turning points of C.

   (2)

2. The curve C has equation $\quad y = 4x^2 + \dfrac{5x-1}{x}.$

   (a) Find $\dfrac{dy}{dx}$.

   (3)

   (b) Find the x-coordinate of the stationary point of C.

   (3)

   (c) Determine whether this stationary point is a maximum or a minimum.

   (2)

This publication may be reproduced only in accordance with Edexcel Limited copyright policy. © 2006 Edexcel limited

3.

Figure 3

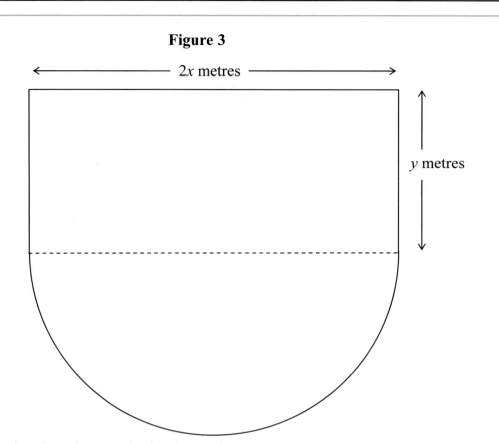

←——————— 2x metres ———————→

y metres

Figure 3 shows the plan of a stage in the shape of a rectangle joined to a semicircle. The length of the rectangular part is 2x metres and the width is y metres. The diameter of the semicircular part is 2x metres. The perimeter of the stage is 80 m.

(a) Show that the area, A m^2, of the stage is given by $A = 80x - \left(2 + \dfrac{\pi}{2}\right)x^2$.

(4)

(b) Use calculus to find the value of x at which A has a stationary value.

(4)

(c) Prove that the value of x you found in part (b) gives the maximum value of A.

(2)

(d) Calculate, to the nearest m^2, the maximum area of the stage.

(2)

1. Given that $y = 2x^2 - \dfrac{6}{x^3}$, $x \neq 0$, evaluate $\displaystyle\int_1^3 y \ dx$.

(4)

2.

Figure 1

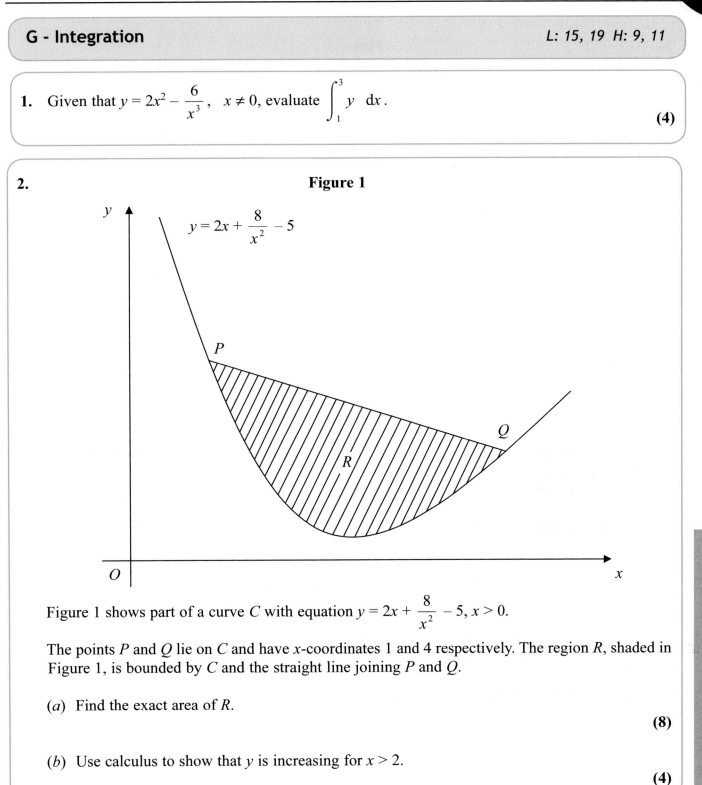

$$y = 2x + \dfrac{8}{x^2} - 5$$

Figure 1 shows part of a curve C with equation $y = 2x + \dfrac{8}{x^2} - 5$, $x > 0$.

The points P and Q lie on C and have x-coordinates 1 and 4 respectively. The region R, shaded in Figure 1, is bounded by C and the straight line joining P and Q.

(a) Find the exact area of R.

(8)

(b) Use calculus to show that y is increasing for $x > 2$.

(4)

3.

Figure 1

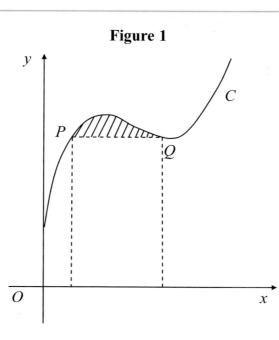

Figure 1 shows a sketch of part of the curve C with equation $y = x^3 - 7x^2 + 15x + 3$, $x \geq 0$.

The point P, on C, has x-coordinate 1 and the point Q is the minimum turning point of C.

(a) Find $\dfrac{dy}{dx}$.

(2)

(b) Find the coordinates of Q.

(4)

(c) Show that PQ is parallel to the x-axis.

(2)

(d) Calculate the area, shown shaded in Fig. 1, bounded by C and the line PQ.

(6)

4.   The speed, v m s^{-1}, of a train at time t seconds is given by

$$v = \sqrt{(1.2^t - 1)}, \quad 0 \leq t \leq 30.$$

The following table shows the speed of the train at 5 second intervals.

t	0	5	10	15	20	25	30
v	0	1.22	2.28		6.11		

(a) Complete the table, giving the values of v to 2 decimal places.

(3)

The distance, s metres, travelled by the train in 30 seconds is given by

$$s = \int_{0}^{30} \sqrt{(1.2^t - 1)} \ dt.$$

(b) Use the trapezium rule, with all the values from your table, to estimate the value of s.

(3)

Core Mathematics C2 - Answers

A - Algebra and functions

1. $a = -7, b = 2$

2. (a) 2

(b) $(x - 1)(2x - 1)(x + 2)$

(c) 3.5

B - Coordinate geometry

1. (a) $(x-4)^2 + (y-3)^2 = (\sqrt{5})^2$

$\Rightarrow x^2 + y^2 - 8x - 6y + 20 = 0$

(b) $(2, 4)$

2. (a) $\sqrt{26}$

(b) $\left(\dfrac{7}{2}, \dfrac{5}{2}\right)$

(c) $(x - 3.5)^2 + (y - 2.5)^2 = 6.5$

3. (a) $(5, 0)$

(b) 4

(c) $(1, 0), \quad (9, 0)$

(d) Radius and tangent perpendicular

$y = -\dfrac{2}{7}(x - 5)$

C - Sequences and series

1. (a) $(S =) \, a + ar + \ldots + ar^{n-1}$

$(rS =) \, ar + ar^2 + \ldots + ar^n$

$S(1 - r) = a(1 - r^n) \quad S = \dfrac{a(1 - r^n)}{1 - r}$

(b) 87.8

(c) 100

(d) $\dfrac{10}{11}$

2. (a) $\dfrac{a}{1 - r} = 480$

$\dfrac{120}{1 - r} = 480 \Rightarrow 120 = 480(1 - r)$

$1 - r = \tfrac{1}{4} \Rightarrow \qquad r = \tfrac{3}{4}$

(b) 9.49

(c) 416

(d) 4

3. (a) $= 1 + 24x + 216x^2 + 864x^3 + 1296x^4$

(b) 130 466 162 401

4. (a) $(1 + px)^9 = 1 + 9px \; ; \; + \binom{9}{2}(px)^2$

(b) $9p = 36, \quad$ so $\underline{p = 4}$

$q = \dfrac{9 \times 8}{2}p^2 \quad$ or $\quad 36p^2 \quad$ or $\quad 36p$

So $\quad q = 576$

D - Trigonometry

1. (a) 0.548

(b) 0.58, 2.56

2.

(a) $\cos A\hat{O}B = \dfrac{5^2 + 5^2 - 6^2}{2 \times 5 \times 5}$ or

$\sin\theta = \frac{3}{5}$ with use of $\cos 2\theta = 1 - 2\sin^2\theta$

$= \dfrac{7}{25}$ *

(b) $A\hat{O}B = 1.2870022...$ radians

(c) Sector $= \frac{1}{2} \times 5^2 \times (b)$, $= 16.087...$

(d) Triangle $= \frac{1}{2} \times 5^2 \times \sin(b)$

or $\frac{1}{2} \times 6 \times \sqrt{5^2 - 3^2}$

Segment = (their sector) – their triangle

= (sector from c) – 12

3. (a) 6.9°, 113.1°

(b) 63.4°, 243.4°, 116.6°, 296.6°

4. (a) 56.3°, 236.6°

(b) 90°, 270°, 60°, 300°

5. (a)

(b) $\left(0, \dfrac{1}{\sqrt{2}}\right)$, $\left(\dfrac{\pi}{4}, 0\right)$, $\left(\dfrac{5\pi}{4}, 0\right)$

(c) $\dfrac{\pi}{12}, \dfrac{17\pi}{12}$

E - Exponentials and logarithms

1. (a) 1.29

(b) $\dfrac{1}{6}$

2. (a) $\dfrac{x+3}{x}$

(b) 0.2

3. (a) $2a - b$

(b) $2 + a + \frac{1}{2}b$

(c) $2a - b = 1$, $2 + a + \frac{1}{2}b = 1$

(d) $b = -1.5$

(e) $x = 0.669$, $y = 0.089$

F - Differentiation

1. (a) $6x^2 - 10x - 4$

(b) $(2, -10)$, $(-\frac{1}{3}, 2\frac{19}{27})$

(c) $12x - 10$

(d) $(2, -10)$ min, $(-\frac{1}{3}, 2\frac{19}{27})$ max

2. (a) $8x + \dfrac{1}{x^2}$

(b) $x = -\frac{1}{2}$

(c) Minimum

3. (a) Perimeter $\Rightarrow 2x + 2y + \pi x = 80$

Area $\rightarrow A = 2xy + \dfrac{1}{2}\pi x^2$

$y = \dfrac{80 - 2x - \pi x}{2}$ and sub in to A

$A = 80x - 2x^2 - \pi x^2 + \dfrac{1}{2}\pi x^2$

i.e. $A = 80x - (2 + \dfrac{\pi}{2})x^2$

(b) 11.2

(c) $\dfrac{d^2 A}{dx^2} = -4 - \pi < 0 \quad \therefore A$ is Max

(d) 448 m^2

G - Integration

1. $14\frac{2}{3}$

2. (a) 6.75

(b) $\dfrac{dy}{dx} = 2 - 16x^{-3}$

(Increasing where) $\dfrac{dy}{dx} > 0$;

For $x > 2$, $\dfrac{16}{x^3} < 2$, $\therefore \dfrac{dy}{dx} > 0$ (Allow $\geq$)

3. (a) $3x^2 - 14x + 15$

(b) $(3, 12)$

(c) $P: x = 1 \qquad y = 12$

(d) $1\dfrac{1}{3}$

4. (a)

t	$=$	15	25	30
v	$=$	3.80	9.72	15.37

(b) $S \approx \frac{1}{2} \times 5$;

$[0 + 15.37 + 2(1.22 + 2.28 + 3.80 + 6.11 + 9.72)]$

$= \frac{5}{2}[61.63] = 154.075$

Core Mathematics C2 - Practice paper

Answers to these practice papers have not been included in this book. Your teacher should have access to the mark schemes through Edexcel Online. Alternatively, visit www.examzone.co.uk to download model answers.

Paper Reference(s)

6664/01

Edexcel GCE

Core Mathematics C2

Advanced Subsidiary

Monday 22 May 2006 – Morning

Time: 1 hour 30 minutes

Materials required for examination	Items included with question papers
Mathematical Formulae (Green)	Nil

Candidates may use any calculator EXCEPT those with the facility for symbolic algebra, differentiation and/or integration. Thus candidates may NOT use calculators such as the Texas Instruments TI 89, TI 92, Casio CFX 9970G, Hewlett Packard HP 48G.

Instructions to Candidates

In the boxes above, write your centre number, candidate number, your surname, initial(s) and signature.
Check that you have the correct question paper.
When a calculator is used, the answer should be given to an appropriate degree of accuracy.
You must write your answer for each question in the space following the question.

Information for Candidates

Full marks may be obtained for answers to ALL questions.
The marks for individual questions and the parts of questions are shown in round brackets: e.g. **(2)**.
There are 10 questions in this question paper. The total mark for this paper is 75.

Advice to Candidates

You must ensure that your answers to parts of questions are clearly labelled.
You must show sufficient working to make your methods clear to the examiner. Answers without working may gain no credit.

Leave
blank

1. Find the first 3 terms, in ascending powers of x, of the binomial expansion of $(2 + x)^6$, giving each term in its simplest form.

(4)

2.   Use calculus to find the exact value of $\displaystyle\int_1^2 \left(3x^2 + 5 + \frac{4}{x^2}\right) dx.$

(5)

3. (i) Write down the value of $\log_6 36$.

(1)

(ii) Express $2 \log_a 3 + \log_a 11$ as a single logarithm to base a.

(3)

4. $$f(x) = 2x^3 + 3x^2 - 29x - 60.$$

(a) Find the remainder when f(x) is divided by (x + 2).

(2)

(b) Use the factor theorem to show that (x + 3) is a factor of f(x).

(2)

(c) Factorise f(x) completely.

(4)

4. $$f(x) = 2x^3 + 3x^2 - 29x - 60.$$

Question 4 continued

5. (a) In the space provided, sketch the graph of $y = 3^x$, $x \in \mathbb{R}$, showing the coordinates of the point at which the graph meets the y-axis.

(2)

(b) Complete the table, giving the values of 3^x to 3 decimal places.

x	0	0.2	0.4	0.6	0.8	1
3^x		1.246	1.552			3

(2)

(c) Use the trapezium rule, with all the values from your table, to find an approximation for the value of $\displaystyle\int_0^1 3^x \, dx$.

(4)

Leave
blank

Question 5 continued

6.   (a)   Given that $\sin \theta = 5\cos \theta$, find the value of $\tan \theta$.

                                                        (1)

   (b)   Hence, or otherwise, find the values of θ in the interval $0 \leqslant \theta < 360°$ for which

$$\sin \theta = 5\cos \theta,$$

       giving your answers to 1 decimal place.

                                                         (3)

Question 6 continued

7.

Figure 1

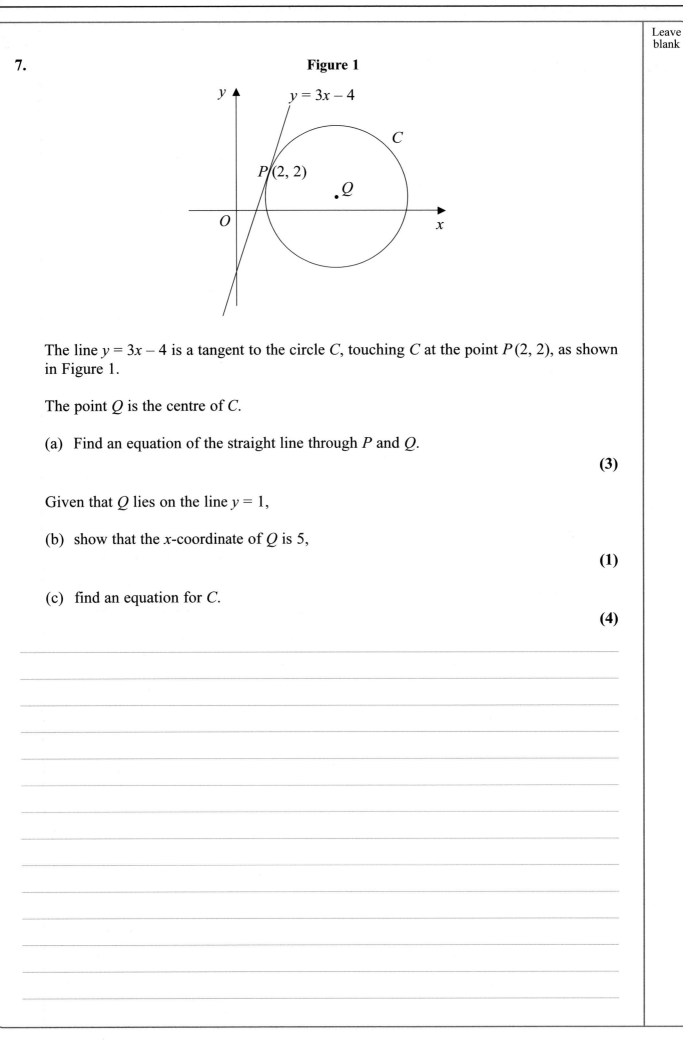

The line $y = 3x - 4$ is a tangent to the circle C, touching C at the point $P(2, 2)$, as shown in Figure 1.

The point Q is the centre of C.

(a) Find an equation of the straight line through P and Q.

(3)

Given that Q lies on the line $y = 1$,

(b) show that the x-coordinate of Q is 5,

(1)

(c) find an equation for C.

(4)

Question 7 continued

8.

Figure 2

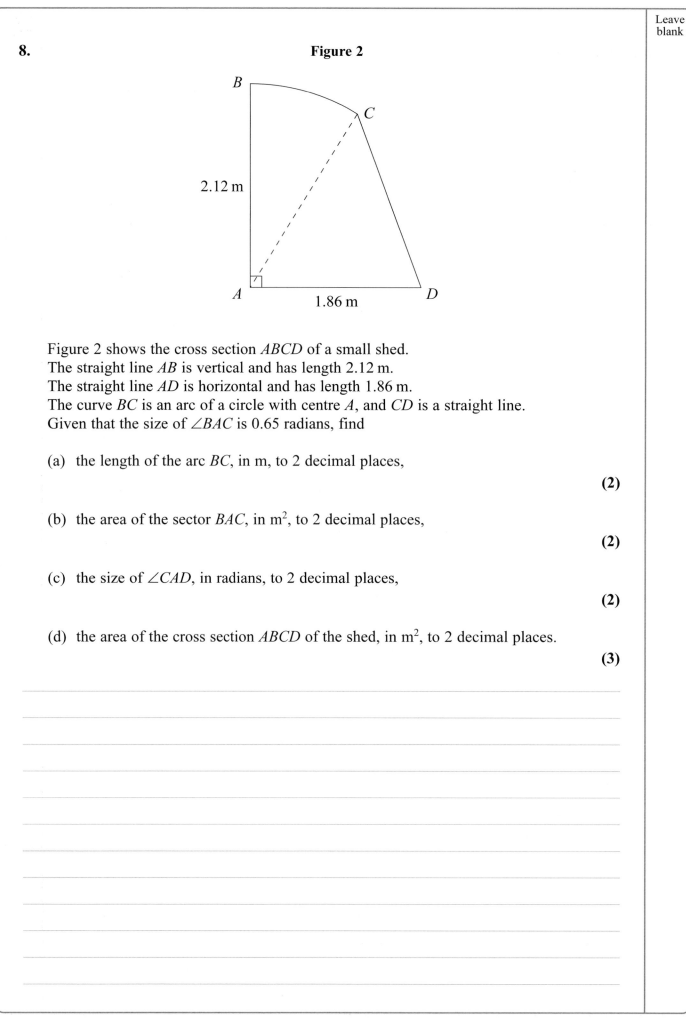

Figure 2 shows the cross section $ABCD$ of a small shed.
The straight line AB is vertical and has length 2.12 m.
The straight line AD is horizontal and has length 1.86 m.
The curve BC is an arc of a circle with centre A, and CD is a straight line.
Given that the size of $\angle BAC$ is 0.65 radians, find

(a) the length of the arc BC, in m, to 2 decimal places,

(2)

(b) the area of the sector BAC, in m², to 2 decimal places,

(2)

(c) the size of $\angle CAD$, in radians, to 2 decimal places,

(2)

(d) the area of the cross section $ABCD$ of the shed, in m², to 2 decimal places.

(3)

Question 8 continued

9. A geometric series has first term a and common ratio r.
The second term of the series is 4 and the sum to infinity of the series is 25.

(a) Show that $25r^2 - 25r + 4 = 0$.

(4)

(b) Find the two possible values of r.

(2)

(c) Find the corresponding two possible values of a.

(2)

(d) Show that the sum, S_n, of the first n terms of the series is given by

$$S_n = 25(1 - r^n).$$

(1)

Given that r takes the larger of its two possible values,

(e) find the smallest value of n for which S_n exceeds 24.

(2)

Leave blank

Question 9 continued

10.

Figure 3

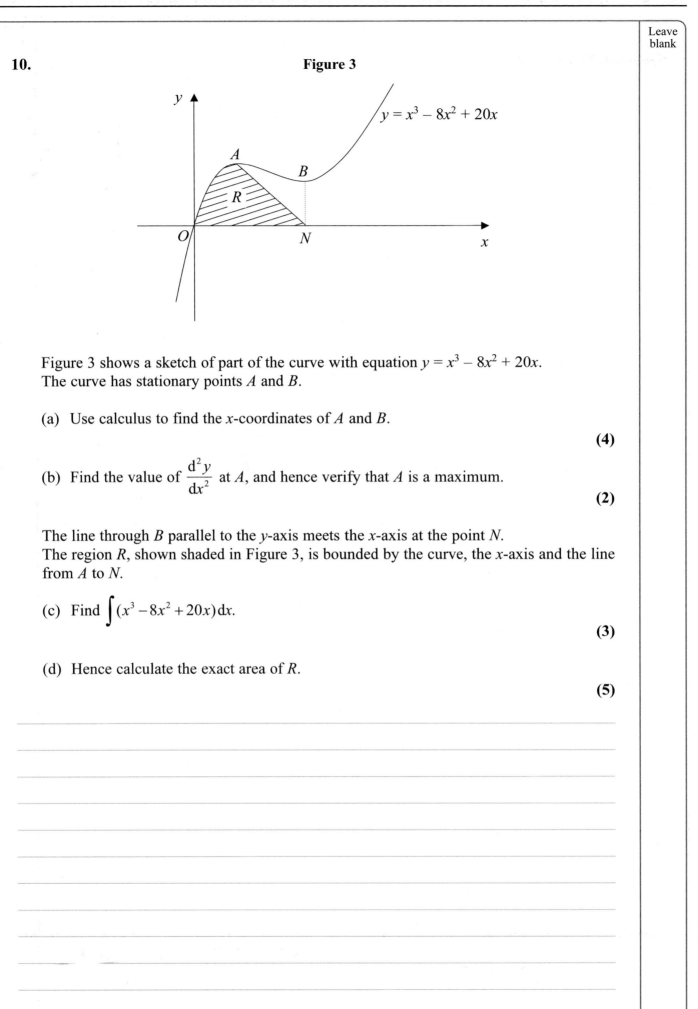

Figure 3 shows a sketch of part of the curve with equation $y = x^3 - 8x^2 + 20x$.
The curve has stationary points A and B.

(a) Use calculus to find the x-coordinates of A and B.

(4)

(b) Find the value of $\dfrac{d^2y}{dx^2}$ at A, and hence verify that A is a maximum.

(2)

The line through B parallel to the y-axis meets the x-axis at the point N.
The region R, shown shaded in Figure 3, is bounded by the curve, the x-axis and the line from A to N.

(c) Find $\displaystyle\int (x^3 - 8x^2 + 20x)\, dx$.

(3)

(d) Hence calculate the exact area of R.

(5)

Leave
blank

Question 10 continued

TOTAL FOR PAPER: 75 MARKS

END

Licence Agreement: *Edexcel Topic Tutor A-Level Maths, Core 1 & Core 2 Student CD-ROM* (ISBN: 978-1-84690-011-2)

Warning:

This is a legally binding agreement between You (the user) and Edexcel Limited, of One90 High Holborn, London, WC1V 7BH, United Kingdom ("Edexcel").

By retaining this Licence, any software media or accompanying written materials or carrying out any of the permitted activities You are agreeing to be bound by the terms and conditions of this Licence. If You do not agree to the terms and conditions of this Licence, do not continue to use the *Edexcel Topic Tutor Student CD-ROM* and promptly return the entire publication (this Licence and all software, written materials, packaging and any other component received with it) with Your sales receipt to Your supplier for a full refund.

Edexcel Topic Tutor Student CD-ROM consists of copyright software and data. The copyright is owned by Edexcel. You only own the disk on which the software is supplied. If You do not continue to do only what You are allowed to do as contained in this Licence you will be in breach of the Licence and Edexcel shall have the right to terminate this Licence by written notice and take action to recover from you any damages suffered by Edexcel as a result of your breach.

Yes, You can:

1. use *Edexcel Topic Tutor Student CD-ROM* on your own personal computer as a single individual user.

No, You cannot:

1. copy *Edexcel Topic Tutor Student CD-ROM* (other than making one copy for back-up purposes);
2. alter the software included on the *Edexcel Topic Tutor Student CD-ROM*, or in any way reverse engineer, decompile or create a derivative product from the contents of the database or any software included in it (except as permitted by law);
3. include any software data from *Edexcel Topic Tutor Student CD-ROM* in any other product or software materials;
4. rent, hire, lend or sell *Edexcel Topic Tutor Student CD-ROM* to any third party;
5. copy any part of the documentation except where specifically indicated otherwise;
6. use the software in any way not specified above without the prior written consent of Edexcel.

Grant of Licence:

Edexcel grants You, provided You only do what is allowed under the Yes, You can section above, and do nothing under the No, You cannot section above, a non-exclusive, non-transferable Licence to use *Edexcel Topic Tutor Student CD-ROM*.
The above terms and conditions of this Licence become operative when using *Edexcel Topic Tutor Student CD-ROM*.

Limited Warranty:
Edexcel warrants that the disk or CD-ROM on which the software is supplied is free from defects in material and workmanship in normal use for ninety (90) days from the date You receive it. This warranty is limited to You and is not transferable.

This limited warranty is void if any damage has resulted from accident, abuse, misapplication, service or modification by someone other than Edexcel. In no event shall Edexcel be liable for any damages whatsoever arising out of installation of the software, even if advised of the possibility of such damages. Edexcel will not be liable for any loss or damage of any nature suffered by any party as a result of reliance upon or reproduction of any errors in the content of the publication.

Edexcel does not warrant that the functions of the software meet Your requirements or that the media is compatible with any computer system on which it is used or that the operation of the software will be unlimited or error free. You assume responsibility for selecting the software to achieve Your intended results and for the installation of, the use of and the results obtained from the software.

Edexcel shall not be liable for any loss or damage of any kind (except for personal injury or death caused by its negligence) arising from the use of *Edexcel Topic Tutor Student CD-ROM* or from errors, deficiencies or faults therein, whether such loss or damage is caused by negligence or otherwise.

The entire liability of Edexcel and your only remedy shall be replacement free of charge of the components that do not meet this warranty.

No information or advice (oral, written or otherwise) given by Edexcel's employees or agents shall create a warranty or in any way increase the scope of this warranty.

To the extent the law permits, Edexcel disclaims all other warranties, either express or implied, including by way of example and not limitation, warranties of quality and fitness for a particular purpose in respect of *Edexcel Topic Tutor Student CD-ROM*.

Governing Law:
This Licence will be governed and construed in accordance with English law.